How To Use This Book

Colour the fabulous scenes with your sparkliest pens and pencils. When you find a section with a dotted outline, it's your turn to complete the drawing. Follow the outline, then use your imagination to doodle and decorate the shape.

Try it out on the picture below.

This beautiful dress is perfect for a princess to wear to a ball. Follow the outline, then decorate with pretty patterns.

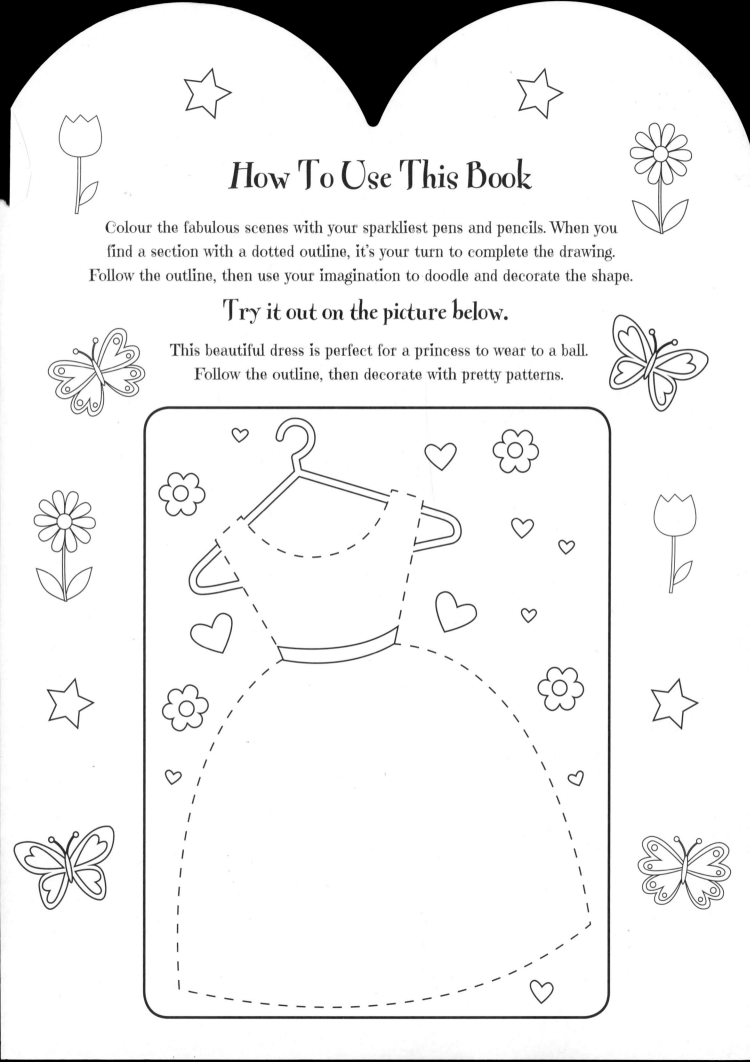

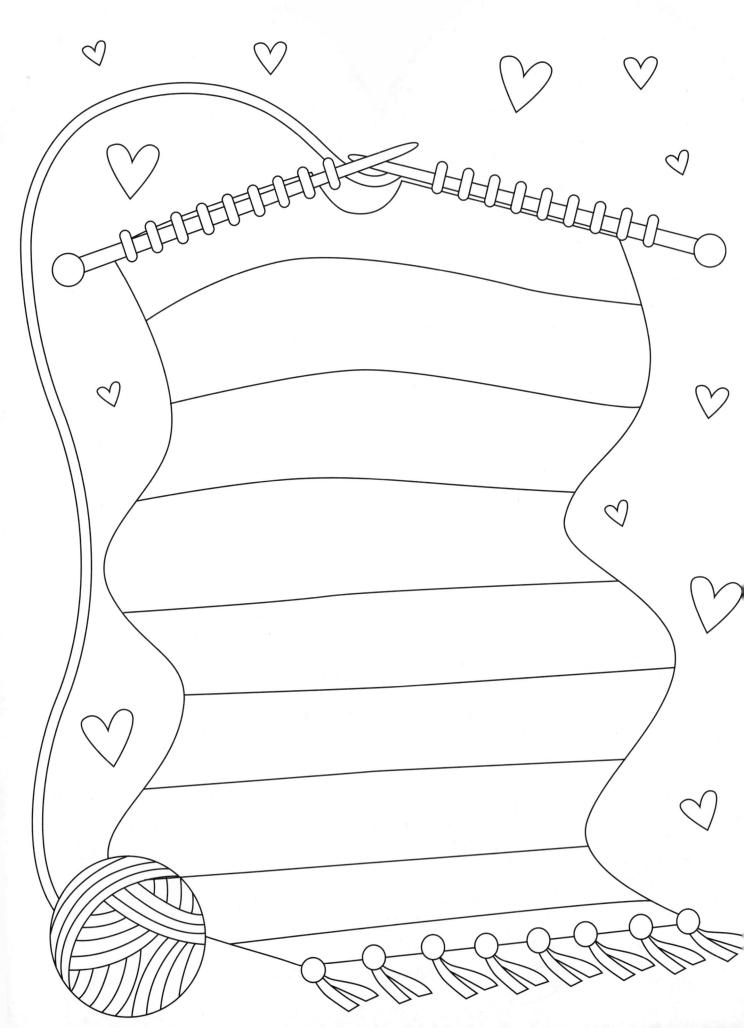